The diary of
A YOUNG SOLDIER IN WORLD WAR I

Editor Louisa Sladen
Editor-in-Chief John C. Miles
Designer Jason Billin/Billin Design Solutions
Art Director Jonathan Hair

First published in 2001
by Franklin Watts
96 Leonard Street
London
EC2A 4XD

Franklin Watts Australia
56 O'Riordan Street
Alexandria
NSW 2015

ISBN 0 7496 4256 4 (hbk)
0 7496 4418 4 (pbk)

Dewey classification: 940.3

A CIP catalogue record for this book is available
from the British Library.

Printed in Great Britain

The diary of A YOUNG SOLDIER IN WORLD WAR I

by Dennis Hamley
Illustrated by Brian Duggan

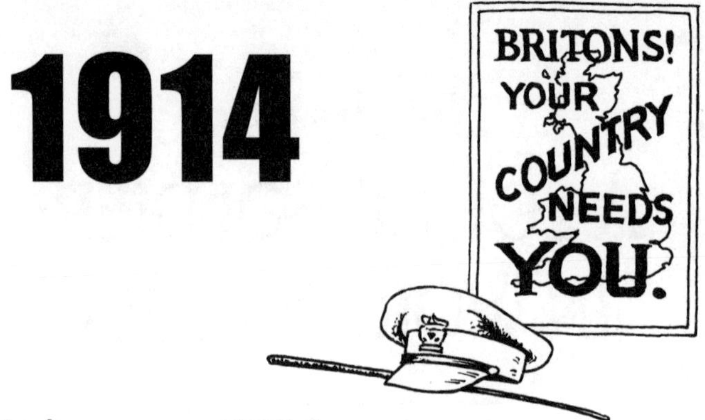

4 August 1914
Todheaton, Yorkshire

It's my seventeenth birthday today, but nobody seems to care except me because everybody says we're going to have a war with Germany. We weren't going to have one yesterday but we are today and if anyone saw it coming they didn't tell me.

If this war is so important that it's made me lose my birthday because of it, I'd better keep a journal about it so I can remind myself why. I'm Billy Warren. I live in Todheaton, in Yorkshire, near the border with Lancashire. I'm tall for my age, I've got fair hair, I love my cricket and football but between you and me I'm a bit shy of the girls still. If having a war means I can get out of here, and have some excitement, then that's all right by me! I left school when I was thirteen and went to work in Burton's engineering factory making machinery for textile mills. Anything would be better than that.

My great-grandad, who's nearly ninety, can't understand why we're on the French side fighting the Germans because he says it's always been the other way round. Grandad Warren says he doesn't know what he's talking about and wasn't his grandad in the army in the Crimean War when the French were our allies? Great-grandad said he supposed so, but then we were fighting the Russians and now they're on our side as well. He says it's not right, all this changing who you're going to fight, and no good will come of it. What I've heard is that the Germans have invaded little Belgium, so we've joined in to help her because years ago we said we would and we can't go back on a promise. It sounds a good reason to me.

I've got a brother called Jack. I look just like him. "Two peas from a pod," people say about us. He is twenty-one and he's in the Territorial Army. The Terriers meet every week at the Drill Hall, march and point rifles at each other. He says he's halfway to being a proper soldier already, but our Dad says he's just playing at it. Last week they went to Wales on a camp, but yesterday they came back, a week before they were supposed to. Jack said he knew something was up even before we heard about the war. He doesn't care who it is we're fighting, he wants to get out there as soon as he can. Anything to get out of this place, go to foreign parts and have a bit of adventure, he says. Mam cried because he was going, but Dad said, "Don't worry, love. He'll be all right. And our Billy can't go. They won't have them if they're not nineteen." Mam cheered up a bit then, but not much. Anyway, that's the first day of the war over and all it's done is make Mam cry and me feel fed up.

6 August 1914

Our Jack went off with the Terriers this morning to training camp on Salisbury Plain. He'll soon be scaring the life out of the Germans, just in time to be home for Christmas, leaving me with no war to go to!

12 August 1914

Wherever I go I see this poster with Lord Kitchener's face on it and his finger pointing at me. "Your Country Wants YOU", the poster says. He's top man in the army. He wants volunteers ready to fight for their country to join a great New Volunteer Army. The British Expeditionary Force may be the best there is but there aren't enough soldiers in it.

It's not so much his pointing finger that makes me feel guilty as those eyes of his which seem to follow me around wherever I go. But I can't join up because I'm only only seventeen.

25 August 1914

The newspapers are full of what's happening in the war. The German army fought all through Belgium and nearly reached Paris, but the French kept them out of the city and now they're pushing them back again. The British haven't done much yet, but that's only because there aren't many of our soldiers there. When there are, things will change, you'll see. Anyway, the British Expeditionary Force – what a mouthful! I'll call it the BEF from now on – it stood firm against the whole German army at Mons and some say an angel appeared in the sky to help them.

8 SEPTEMBER 1914

Big things happened in Todheaton today. There was a meeting in the Town Hall. Hundreds went and I was one of them. On the stage was a table with a Union Jack draped over it. Behind the table sat an officer, in a smart uniform with rings on his sleeves and his swagger stick on the table in front of him. But he was old and I could see why he wasn't over in France now. Also behind the table were the vicar, Mr Burton, who owns the factory where most men in Todheaton work, and Lord Bowland, a big man round these parts who's in the government.

First, the officer talked about the great history of the British Army, how it is the best in the world and he was proud to be in it and so should everyone else be. Then the vicar said how we were fighting on God's side against the devil and all his works and if anyone wanted to see who the devil was he only had to look at what was happening in Belgium now. Mr Burton said that Lord Kitchener's New Volunteer Army would give all young men who wanted adventure their chance.

Then Lord Bowland stood up. "Young men of Todheaton," he said. "Your country calls you. Already in cities and towns round about, battalions of comrades are being raised."
Well, we'd all heard of them, the Barnsley Pals, the Leeds Pals, the Manchester Pals,

the Liverpool Pals, the Sheffield Pals and the Accrington Pals. "Why not," he said, "the Todheaton Pals?"

You should have heard the cheering. When it stopped, the officer stepped forward to say that all able-bodied men between the ages of nineteen and thirty should give their names in now and go to the Territorial Army Drill Hall tomorrow. A few dithered, but most stepped forward. I saw a few who I knew weren't nineteen yet. So I thought, if they can, so can I, and I gave my name in with the rest.

Mam was furious. "It's bad enough our Jack's joined up. I don't want Billy to go as well," she shouted. Then she started crying again.

"Don't worry, lass," said our Dad. "He's too young. They won't look at him."

9 September 1914

I can't believe what happened today. I queued up with all the rest, waiting to see the recruiting sergeant. When it was my turn, I stepped up to him and said, "I want to join as well. I'm old enough."

He looked at me as if he knew I wasn't telling the truth. Then he said, "Are you now? How old are you really, sonny?"

I didn't dare lie after all. So I answered, "Seventeen last month."

"Hmmm," he said. "Take a deep breath." I did. "Deeper," he shouted. "Deeper." I was nearly bursting. "Right, let it out," he said. When I had, he said, "Now do it again."

So I did, and when I'd finished, he said. "My, you did well then, sonny. I reckon you put on a year for each breath. You're nineteen already. Well done, lad, you're in."

My best mates, Tommy Braithwaite and Fred Oughton, did some deep breathing for the sergeant as well, so they're both in. We're three privates in the Twenty-fifth (Todheaton) Battalion of the Loyal Yorks and Lancs Light Infantry and a finer regiment, so they tell us, you'll never find. The three of us have vowed to stick together through thick and thin. I thought it must be a funny old army if they let you in even when you're not old enough, but I felt really pleased, even though our Mam nearly flooded the kitchen out with her crying.

"Don't worry, lass," said our Dad. "He'll never fire a rifle. The war will be over by Christmas."

14 September 1914

I was right, it is a funny old army. All us volunteers have had to leave home and sleep on the floor in the Town Hall. A few real old sweats from the Boer War have put their uniforms on again to train us. Tommy dared to tell Sergeant Major Wardle that it was daft sleeping on bare boards when he could be snug in his house down the next street. The Sergeant Major, who's got more medals on his chest than the King has jewels in his crown, didn't shout. He just told

Tommy that this wasn't the Town Hall any more. He was sleeping under the King's roof now and he should be proud. That shut Tommy up all right.

Still, what is this training? Marching up and down the road, practising about-turns and forming fours on the Drill Hall parade ground, with no uniforms and no rifles. I reckon when Dad said I'd never fire a rifle, he was about right. I'm wondering why I bothered.

15 November 1914

I've not written much in my diary recently because there's not much to say. The war doesn't seem to be getting anywhere, though the papers keep talking about great victories.

We're still in the Town Hall and we still haven't got rifles. But we have got uniforms. No, not khaki ones. Mr Burton had some tailor run them up for us cheap out of some spare blue cloth he had. We look like postmen, not soldiers. Still, we did have a parade through the town yesterday. I heard some kids shouting "Look, look, the soldiers are coming," but then one said, "They're not soldiers, they're only the Todheaton Pals." I felt a right fool.

27 December 1914

Well, that's the first Christmas of the war over. They let me go the whole half mile home and Christmas with our Mam and Dad was lovely. But the war isn't over like they said it would be and our Jack didn't come home, though he's not in France yet but stuck on Salisbury Plain in a tent. But they do say we'll be going off to camp ourselves soon.

1915

25 January 1915

Jack wrote to tell us that his battalion is finally off to France. The last words in his letter were, "I pray to God that I'll be home to see you soon all in one piece and that I never have to leave you again."

It doesn't sound as if he's too happy. I feel good, though. The Todheaton Pals are off to Wales for training. At last we'll feel like real soldiers!

25 February 1915
Llandudno, North Wales

Today we arrived in Llandudno, by the sea. We came by train, more than a thousand of us in the battalion, with thirty-six officers. It was a cold, snowy day. We formed up early this morning outside the drill hall and then marched through the streets to the railway station, headed by the town brass band. When we got on the train at Todheaton, it felt like we were on the way to France already, with all the people

who came to see us off, mothers and fathers, wives having a last kiss, little children waving and shouting and wondering what it was all about. Yet we weren't even wearing khaki. We were still in our blue uniforms like postmen and there wasn't a single rifle between us.

When we arrived, we split up on the station platform into our companies and then into our platoons. I can never remember which is which, so I'd better write them down while they are fresh in my mind. In the New Army there are four or five companies in every battalion and each company is supposed to have 250 men in it.

Captain Cunliffe is the company commander. Though he's not an officer like the ones in the BEF. He was just a manager at Burtons who's put a uniform on and he'll have to learn what to do the same as we will. Each company has four platoons, with about sixty men in each one, and each platoon has four sections. The platoon commander is Lieutenant Askew. He's the vicar's son. There are fifteen men in my section. Sergeant Pickering is in charge of it – he's a real old soldier and knows more than any of the officers. Corporal Naylor is second-in-command, though Tommy Braithwaite says he's useless and I think I agree with him. We expected to be in huts like in a proper camp, but instead we are billeted in people's houses. Sounds all right to me.

27 February 1915

Some of us haven't come off very well out of living in people's houses. They've got mean landladies who give them rotten food. I stuck fast to my best mates, Tommy and Fred, and we've been put into rooms over a sweetshop, living with the shopkeeper and his wife. They're lovely. The shopkeeper let us fill our pockets up with sweets for free this morning before we went on parade and Fred said, "If this is what being in the army's like, I should have joined up years ago."

28 February 1915

Today, we had a big parade in the town square and all the townsfolk came out to see it. Then we went on a route march all round Wales, it seemed, though Fred thinks Corporal Naylor got us lost. Tonight, Tommy and I have been put on guard duty, to make sure no Germans try to land on the pier – so they tell us. That's where I'm writing now, though I'll put the diary away quick if an officer comes by. We haven't got rifles, but if any Germans turn up, I'm sure we can knock them on the head with the chairlegs we've been given instead. Our orders are to look out for submarines. We'll see their periscopes sticking out of the water. If any have come to Llandudno, they're staying well under it.

2 March 1915

There was great excitement today. Our new Battalion Commanding Officer arrived to take over. He's no factory owner or solicitor with a uniform on. He is a real soldier, Colonel Elliott, and the moment we saw him in his uniform on his horse, we knew we'd joined the proper army. Khaki uniforms and rifles won't be far away now!

15 March 1915

Our proper khaki uniforms are here. Farewell to the postmen. Hooray!

We got our full pack as well to sling on our shoulders. When it's loaded with everything the army says we've got to carry, the whole lot weighs nearly half as much as we do. I don't fancy running into battle with that lot weighing me down.

16 March 1915

At last. Today we were issued with rifles and bayonets. They are old-fashioned, worn-out things. When Tommy got his, he said, "I wonder how many of Napoleon's soldiers this one shot?"

I'm beginning to think the army is in a bit of a mess. I bet the Germans don't have to put up with guns as bad as these. Still, at least we can go on the rifle range looking more like proper soldiers.

Today we were told how to strip the rifles

down and clean them. We listened very carefully. We all know that for a soldier at war, his rifle is his greatest friend.

17 March 1915

This morning we started bayonet practice. Sacks stuffed with straw were hung in front of us and we had to run screaming up to them and stab them as if they were the enemy. I don't suppose real Germans will stand there like stuffed sacks, but you never know your luck.

This afternoon we were on the rifle range shooting at targets for the first time. I loved it.

Although my old rifle is worn out and nearly falling to bits, I reckon I'll be a crack shot when I've finished. Sergeant Pickering thinks so, anyway.

14 April 1915

I'm home on leave. It's good to be back and seeing everyone.

I haven't written anything for a long time because I haven't had the heart to. We're hearing bad things from the Front in France. Terrible battles with thousands killed and no land gained. Poison gas used. Jack's letters to Mam and Dad don't say much except that he's keeping as well as can be expected, whatever that means. When I read them, I feel a shiver. It's mostly fun with my mates in the army now, but will it always be like this?

15 April 1915

Jack turned up on leave today. He's only here for a few days, because though his leave is nine days long, it took him three days to get here. He brought his rifle and pack with him, but he wouldn't let me look at the rifle. "Leave it alone," he shouted. "I didn't bring it here for fun." I only wanted to see what a really good new one was like. He looks twenty years older.

I thought he'd tell me all about what I could expect when I got to France, but he won't say a thing. Except for his rifle, it's as if he doesn't care about anything any more.

20 April 1915

He left yesterday. Seeing him go was the worst moment of our lives. He looked so unhappy. I wish I knew what he was feeling. I didn't sleep all night for thinking about him. I'm going back to Llandudno today. Jack not talking hasn't made me feel very happy about it.

23 April 1915

Back in Llandudno, to find news waiting. We're leaving Wales and going back north to Ripon Camp in Yorkshire. "A real army camp at last," Sergeant Pickering told us. "And may God help you." No more free sweets in the morning, no more seaside piers to guard. Ah well!

1 May 1915
Ripon Camp, Yorkshire

Ripon Camp. What a dump. There was nothing ready for us - no bedding, no food, no light. Is this what Sergeant Pickering meant by "a real army camp"? Colonel Elliott was furious. He never took his pack off until after midnight. He went round sorting things out, banging heads together if he had to, until we were all settled. Sometimes, the army seems hopeless. I hope things are better organised in France.

We sleep in big wooden huts, thirty to a hut. There are thousands of soldiers here from all over the country and every one of them looks fed up. At least it makes us feel we really belong in the army.

4 August 1915

We've been at camp a long time. Now it's my eighteenth birthday and the war's first. I had a few beers in the YMCA with Fred and Tommy but I really didn't feel like celebrating. I never thought I'd say it, but we don't half miss Todheaton.

27 August 1915

I haven't written for a long time, because there is nothing to write about. Drill, route marches, target practice (I'm a real crack shot now), bayonet practice, on and on and on and on. "You've got to get used to it," Sergeant Pickering said today. "Army life is 99 per cent complete boredom, one per cent absolute panic."

23 September 1915

Something to relieve the boredom. Today we had training on the Lewis gun. This is a machine gun which needs a team of four to work it, but when you see what it can do, you realise that it is certain death to get in the way of one. We imagined mowing hundreds of the enemy down with it and that made us feel quite good.

5 October 1915

I can't take it in. Our Jack is dead. I had a letter from Mam this morning. He was killed in the Battle of Loos in Belgium. It seems he was in an attack on Hill 70, a high point occupied by the Germans. Our Jack's battalion took the hill and carried on with their advance. But the Germans had prepared new positions further back, defended with barbed wire and bristling with machine guns. Even so, Jack's battalion was ordered to advance on it. They never had a chance. Most of them were killed. I thought of our Lewis gun and wondered what it would be like to advance on to a line of machine guns like it, all firing at me.

I thought of something else as well. My father and mother only have me left now. I must look after myself and make sure I come home safely to Todheaton. Life is very serious, all of a sudden.

25 October 1915
Larkhill Camp, Salisbury Plain

Another move, this time to Larkhill. We're getting nearer to France and what we joined for. Nobody stays here long. We just keep training while we wait for our orders to go. I'll be glad. I've been in the army over a year and not seen one German yet. I'll look after myself. What happened to Jack isn't going to happen to me. Besides, I have to send a few of the enemy to where they sent him.

12 December 1915

No Christmas at home for me this year. I'm almost glad. Without Jack it would be a very sad time. I couldn't bear it for Mam and Dad to have to watch me go off to France as well.

21 December 1915
Etaples army base, Northern France

Our first night in France. We are at a huge army base, the biggest one of all, at Etaples near Calais. They call it the Bull Ring and we've been told to expect the hardest training of all before we go to the Front.

We left Larkhill while it was still dark. We filed down to the long troop train waiting in the siding and then it steamed off on the slow journey to Dover and the troopship to take us across the Channel. There was nobody to see us off. It almost felt as if nobody cared.

1916

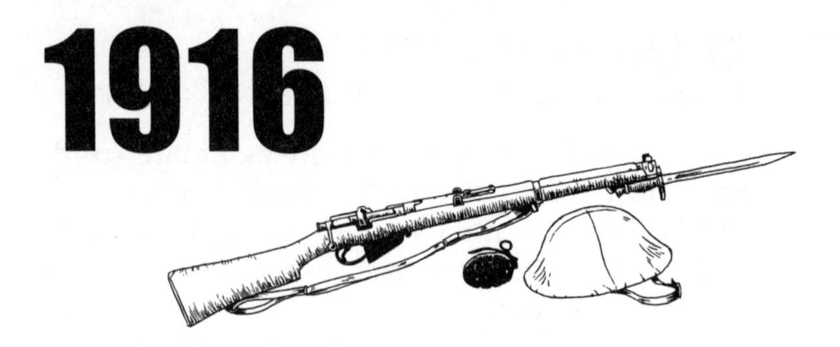

15 January 1916
Etaples army base

We've been here three weeks and this is the first time I haven't felt too tired to write in my diary at night. I'm in a foreign country at last, but I may as well be back at home for all I see of it, except when we have a bit of time off in the town, have a few drinks, hear everybody jabbering away in French and send some patriotic postcards home.

The Bull Ring is hard. Compared with it, all the training back in England seems for children. We have new rifles and Lewis guns to get used to. Our instructors know how to make us sweat. But we can see the point. There are trenches dug to face each other, like the real British and German trenches, with no man's land in between. We dig more trenches, learn to lay barbed wire, practise raiding parties on the trenches opposite and throw Mills bombs. These are hand grenades and once you've pulled the pin you have to let it go or you'll go up with it. We have huge exercises with the whole battalion and sometimes with all the brigade. This must be more like the real war we'll soon be in.

17 February 1916

When Sergeant Pickering said I was a crack shot, I thought I would be made a sniper, with a rifle with the new telescopic sights picking off any enemy soldier fool enough to show his head. Then, when the Lewis guns arrived, I thought perhaps I could be a machine gunner. That way I could kill the enemy the same way they had killed Jack. But someone high up has decided I'm to be none of those things. I'm one of the poor old infantry, ready to raid the trenches with everybody else. I'm glad really. I won't lose touch with Tommy and Fred. In this war you need to stick with your mates.

10 March 1916

There are rumours that we'll be leaving Etaples soon. Something big is going to happen. The French are in trouble. They have lost thousands of men defending a fortress hundreds of miles south of here – Verdun. They can't go on like this. So far, they've borne the brunt of the fighting. Now the British have to do as much if not more as the French have.

Fred said, "That means we'll have all the dirty work now."

Tommy replied, "Go on, Fred. You know it's what you joined for!"

When he said that, I felt my stomach turn over. We will be taking over some of the French positions. Nobody knows where yet, but we do know the name of the river that flows nearby. It is called the Somme.

24 March 1916

We leave Etaples tomorrow. We go by train to Abbeville, then we march to who knows where?

25 March 1916

A village somewhere behind the lines

Well, we've reached somewhere, but I'm not sure where it is. We crowded on to the train at six o'clock this morning. We weren't in proper coaches. They put us in trucks with *Chevaux 8 Hommes 40* painted on the side. "What does that mean?" Fred asked Sergeant Pickering. "It says they can put eight horses or forty men in one of these trucks. Now you know who the army thinks is most important," he answered. "They have to keep the horses comfortable." Judging by the smell and the straw on the floor, the horses had only just got off.

The train steamed along painfully slowly, going south, through Amiens and Abbeville, jolting us so much that once Tommy shouted, "Has this train got square wheels?" Sometimes we stopped miles from anywhere for hours at a time. In mid-afternoon we came to a little place called Pont Remy. Here, sergeants and corporals rushed up and down the platform screaming at us to get off. We stumbled out, formed into some sort of marching order and set off. Even though the weather was biting cold, with sixty-six pounds on our backs and seven miles to march we soon felt very hot. We were also itching all over, but it wasn't until we reached our new billets that we knew why.

We marched for an hour at a time along roads lined with poplar trees, and wide, flat fields either side, then stopped for ten minutes.

Sergeant Pickering told us to lie on our packs and put our feet up so they rested on hedges and fences. This way, the blood flowed away from our feet so that they cooled down. Without doing that, I don't think we could have lasted out. After three hours we came to a village and stopped. The field kitchens were not far behind and the cooks soon got a hot meal for us. Then we looked for shelter for the night. The officers and sergeants stayed in the houses of the villagers, but us ordinary soldiers had to find what we could. Fred, Tommy and I and fifty others chose a barn with straw to sleep on. But we soon found the straw was filthy and rats were everywhere. We also found why we itched. LICE!

They get everywhere. The only way you can get rid of them is to spread your clothes out and burn them out of the lining with candles, taking care you don't set your clothes on fire. Or, if you're really patient, you can scrape the eggs away and kill them. These lice are real little vampires and if you pop them you can get a nasty eyeful of blood.

27 March 1916

We've been on the move for two days, marching on with full packs through little villages where the French are very kind to us. Old ladies press food on us and give us mugs of cider to drink as we march. You realise that they are thinking of their own sons and grandsons far away, perhaps at Verdun, and hoping others are being as kind to them.

It was cold yesterday as we set out and for a long time, to warm ourselves up, we sang soldiers' songs like "It's a Long Way to Tipperary" and "Pack up Your Troubles in Your Old Kit Bag". Sometimes we started on one the officers think is bad for morale. It goes, "You can send my sister, my brother, my auntie or my mother, but for Gawd's sake don't send me!" But as the day went on, we sang less, because we knew that every step took us nearer to the front line. When we finally stopped we sang another song officers don't like, to the tune of "Auld Lang Syne":

"WE'RE HERE BECAUSE
WE'RE HERE BECAUSE
WE'RE HERE BECAUSE
WE'RE HERE."

28 March 1916
Behind the front line

So this is it. The villages round here are ruined by German gunfire and empty. There are no more ordinary French people to give us food or bring us mugs of cider. New roads and railways are being laid: trains arrive with huge guns loaded on them. Ammunition dumps are being built and field hospitals as well. New battalions are constantly arriving. The whole of the army must be coming to the Somme. They say the Somme is an easy, quiet place. I don't think it will be for long. You can tell something big is going to happen soon.

28 March 1916

Out early on parade this morning, then we were detailed for fatigue parties digging new communication trenches. Nobody dares move above the ground now: they would be targets for enemy fire. Going forward through trenches with your head below ground level is the only way. So we dig and dig and dig all day.

4 April 1916
Front-line trench at the Somme

Today I feel as though the war has really started for me. I am writing this in a dugout by the light of a stump of candle because for the first time we are in a front-line trench. We were told on April Fools' Day that we would be relieving another battalion. There are three lines of trenches, reserve trenches, support trenches and front-line trenches. That night we moved up into the reserve lines. We walked for miles along the dark communication trenches, some of which we had dug ourselves, and then bedded down for the night in the third line of trenches. I say "bedded down", but what was it but finding some spot in a dugout in the rear trench wall that wasn't too muddy and curling up as best we could?

All night we listened to the crump of shells from the big guns and bursts of machine-gun fire. Not many of us slept, worn out though we were. I certainly didn't. Next day we cleaned our rifles, got used to being in a trench and just waited. It's quiet in no man's land between us and the Germans. Knowing the enemy is hardly a hundred yards away makes me feel very strange. Am I frightened? I don't know. What will I be like when my turn comes to go into action?

After a two-day wait, tonight we moved up into the front-line trench. On the way up the communication trench we stopped and waited while the soldiers we were relieving filed past us. They were very quiet. The night was cold and clear and in the moonlight I could see their drawn faces. I was reminded of Jack on his last leave. One of them muttered to me, "It might sound peaceful out there but I've lost two of my best mates. Still, not to worry. Fritz will leave you alone until you've had your breakfast and he's had his." Another whispered, "If you don't get trodden on in the mud, it's the rats in the trench you've got to worry about."

We can still hear occasional guns and see the night sky lighting up. The usual tour of duty in the trenches for a battalion is eight to ten days.

Now we filed into the trench. This is where, except for sentry duty, wiring parties at night to keep the barbed wire in order and an occasional trench raid on the enemy, we'll stay – until we are relieved. What a mess. Mud over our ankles, rats as big as your head ready to grab every bit of food, and lice twenty times as bad as the ones we killed in the barn on the way here.

They say this is part of the front where not much happens. Even so, I feel pretty scared.

5 April 1916

When the sun rose this morning and we were told to stand to, I saw no man's land for the first time. Horrible. A sea of mud, tree stumps, shell holes and bodies. Not just whole bodies but bits of them half buried. And this is supposed to be an easy number. Oh my God.

6 April 1916

I don't think I'll ever get used to the rations they send up to the trenches. The bread might have started off fresh but it's four days old when we get it. We also have jars of plum and apple jam, tins of bully beef and more tins of Maconochies. It's the Maconochies I hate most. It's supposed to be pork and beans. More like grease and beans. You can just about get it down you if it's heated up first. But try it cold and it makes you want to throw up.

7 April 1916

Last night, Corporal Naylor detailed Fred and me to go out on sentry duty into a little trench leading off from ours right out into no man's land called a sap. We couldn't have been more than fifty yards from the German trenches. We could hear them talking, singing and laughing. They sound like ordinary men, just like us. It makes you wonder what this war is for.

It was freezing cold. We had to wait, crouching there, watching for suspicious enemy movements. They might start a trench raid on us. After a while you don't know what you're looking for. I got jumpy. I kept thinking I saw something move and nearly shot at it. I stopped just in time because there was never anything there. I was imagining German raiding parties but if I'd fired my rifle I'd give away where we were and that would be the end of us.

I was shivering when I got back to the main trench and it wasn't just from cold. Yet, I thought, that's nothing to what we're in for soon.

9 April 1916

It was my turn to go on wiring duty last night. The barbed wire in front of our trenches has been cut by Germans on trench raids and broken by gunfire in several places. All front line trenches have barriers of barbed wire in front of them. Wooden stakes are hammered in the ground and the wire is tied round them so attacking soldiers will get stuck on it. It's not just a fence. This wire goes out fifty feet or more in front of the trenches. As soon as it was dark, Sergeant Pickering led us out, ten of us. I was next to little Elias Thornley. We worked all night and soon we realised that a German wiring party was working on their wire not a hundred yards away.

Elias was scared. "They know we're here. They're going to shoot us," he kept muttering until Sergeant Pickering hissed, "Shut up, Thornley, or I'll shoot you myself." Well, they never did shoot. I suppose they were as keen on getting their wire right as we were. Much more important than a few dead soldiers here and there. But Elias was no use. He was a quivering wreck when we got back. I'm worried about him.

10 April 1916

We had a big scare today. We were issued with shovels and picks and were repairing the parapet of the trench, the bit at the front built up over the ground with sandbags. Suddenly the Germans started an artillery bombardment. There was a roar in the sky like an express train coming at us fast. Then everything blew up round us as a shell crashed just a few yards away. We dived for the nearest dugout and put our spades over our heads for protection. We were nearly buried in earth.

We had to listen to shells crashing on the trench further down and hoped that no more came near us, because if it did then for sure we'd have been buried alive and worse. After a while the bombardment stopped. It was only a little one after all, or so we thought. But then a messenger came down the line and spoke to Sergeant Pickering. When he'd gone Sergeant Pickering said, "I don't like to tell you this, but three lads further up the line have been killed and the Germans will probably be doing a lot of that now."

"Strewth," said Ted. "What will it be like when the big guns really start firing?"

11 April 1916

The Germans won't let us forget that they are there. Today they were sending over their bombs and shells. They seem to have a lot of them: mortars, minenwerfers and whizz-bangs and, worst of all, great tin drums full of explosive, old nails and anything sharp which can spray itself around. The army calls them canister bombs. We call them "Piss-cans". They've caused some nasty injuries. "Have we just got to sit here while they bomb and shell us whenever they like?" Tommy complained to Sergeant Pickering. "You'll just sit here and take it," said Sergeant Pickering. "Them up top will tell us when to move."

"You mean the staff officers, in a chateau miles away where it's safe, drinking wine and looking at their maps?" Tommy answered angrily. "What do they know?"

I thought Sergeant Pickering would come down hard on Tommy for insubordination. But he never said a word. You can see that he agrees.

12 April 1916

One thing we must not do is put our heads over the parapet of the trench. German snipers are always ready to shoot. They are crack shots and don't often miss. Corporal Naylor forgot how often he'd been telling us and tried to take a crafty look. A bullet got him right between the eyes. It's not right to be nasty now, but Tommy did say he was useless. Still, seeing him dead like that when he'd been on at us to be careful not two minutes before shook us rigid. It's the first death in our company and it made us go cold.

13 April 1916

Something even worse happened today. Little Elias Thornley got a letter from home. His wife's gone off with someone else. As if he wasn't in a bad enough state already. Before anyone could stop him he jumped over the top of the trench, took his boots off, lay down in no man's land, put the barrel of his rifle in his mouth and pulled the trigger with his toe. He was dead at once. I'd heard of men shooting themselves to be out of the war but I never believed it. None of us could speak as we buried him. The Germans must have seen what happened and understood. There wasn't a single shot at us while we brought him back. I don't know what Lieutenant Askew will put in his letter to his family back home. I still feel shaken and very, very sad. But I think he's better off now.

14 April 1916

I feel as if we're here in the trench just waiting to be shot at and I want to be doing something. We're getting jumpy and nervous.

But now the generals back in the chateaux must have decided it's time we hit back a bit. This afternoon Lieutenant Askew asked for volunteers for a trench raiding party, to let the Germans know we weren't just cannon fodder. We would take them by surprise, cause as much damage and death as we could and then get out quick.

I volunteered at once and so did Fred and Tommy. I'm writing this before we go, having just got ready. There are thirty of us going. First we took the buttons and badges off our uniforms and paybooks and personal letters out of our pockets so the enemy won't know what regiment we're from if we're captured or killed. We've taken all our equipment off except rifle and bayonet, but some of us have made heavy clubs out of bits of wood, fit to smash anybody's head in. I'm taking my old sheathknife and so is anybody else who has one. We've got Mills bombs attached to our belts ready to throw and a few bombs of our own, home-made out of jam pots filled with gun cotton and nails. We've smeared our faces with burnt cork and now we're waiting for Lieutenant Askew to give the order.

15 April 1916

It's morning. I'm back alive and untouched and I've got to write this down because I'll never understand it if I don't.

Lieutenant Askew led us over the top of the trench and we crawled under our wire out into no man's land. Then we inched our way across, through shell holes full of stinking mud. Sometimes I came across a body and it was all I could do not to cry out. We expected the Germans at any moment to send up flares which would light no man's land up and show where we were. But they didn't and we got through the German wire, cutting it with wire-cutters and lighting a few Bangalore torpedoes to break it a bit more. Surely the Germans must have known we were there. When we reached their trenches, we jumped in screaming our heads off. Lieutenant Askew was in front firing his revolver. Behind him were two men with rifles and bayonets ready, then came the bomber with the Mills bombs and jam pots. I came just after, with Tommy and Fred. But did we surprise the Germans? Did we heck.

They'd seen us and were waiting. The noise was terrible, our Mills bombs were exploding

and the Germans were firing. Their machine guns started up and I thought we were finished before we'd started.

I couldn't see anybody, but suddenly there was a dark figure in front of me. He had his bayonet drawn. So here I was, fighting an enemy soldier in the dark and I knew it was him or me. The first German I'd come across and I couldn't even see him. I stabbed at him with my own bayonet and suddenly I heard a sort of gurgle and then he wasn't there. I must have killed him. I suddenly thought of Jack. Perhaps that was a little bit of revenge. Then, without any warning, the noise stopped.

When the smoke cleared I seemed to be the only one moving. I saw bodies sprawled all round me. There was groaning from injured men, ours and German. Was I the only one left? Lieutenant Askew had been killed with a bayonet. I looked for Fred and Tommy. Tommy was dead: I could see there was no hope for him. Then I found Fred. He was sprawled on the trench floor covered in blood, but I could see he was alive. I pulled him up by the shoulders and somehow got him over the parapet of the trench. Then I had to pull him over the mud, under the wire and across no man's land. I can't believe no Germans saw me. I reckon they let me go on purpose. I dragged Fred as far as I could to a shell hole. Then I must have passed out.

The next I knew it was getting light and

Sergeant Pickering was in the shell hole with a stretcher party. "Come on back, lad," he said. "Your mate will be looked after now. He'll be in hospital and out of the war for a while."

When I got back to the trench, all I could do was cry. I can't take it all in. My best mate Tommy is dead. First Jack, now him. And for what? What has all that effort done? We've lost a good officer, a lot of men and one of my two greatest friends, for nothing. They say these raids are to keep our fighting spirits up. Well, it's certainly knocked mine right out of me.

16 April 1916

Our first tour of duty in the firing trench is over. The lads from Huddersfield have relieved us. Fred's back behind the lines in the field hospital and I think he'll be sent home to Blighty. I wish I was going with him. If this part of the front is an easy number, I don't want to see one where it's hotted up.

20 June 1916

Warnimont Wood, seven miles behind the lines

I've written nothing for two months. To start with I was too upset about Tommy and Fred. Fred will be in England now, I hope. I wish I was with him. With any luck he won't come back, because we're going on the big offensive soon, which they say will win the war for us.

We've been training for it here in the reserve lines ever since, so we all know what we've got to do. It will be easy, they tell us. First, there's going to be an artillery bombardment on the German trenches. Nearly every gun the army has got will pour shells down on them for a week or more. Nothing will be able to survive. When it's over, their barbed wire will be smashed and there will be no resistance because all the Germans will be dead. All we have to do is to march forward, take their empty trenches and then carry on to Berlin. The war will be over in a few months.

We have a timetable to keep. We have an hour to take the trenches, another half hour to reach the next village and so on. It sounds as though it's really well planned this time. It has to succeed. We all feel happy. Home for Christmas. Wouldn't that be wonderful?

We've rehearsed the attack time after time. We marched forward slowly towards some ditches dug to show where the enemy trenches will be. Then orders were shouted and we all wheeled about as if we were doing drill on the parade ground. Time and time again we did it. It seemed so easy. They tell us no Germans will be left to fire on us and nothing can go wrong. I hope they're right.

22 JUNE 1916

We're waiting to go up into the line. We've been put in wooden huts which are a disgrace. They have no windows, no lights, no fires. We have hardly any bedding and the nights are cold. Those huts we complained about last year in Ripon seem like Buckingham Palace by comparison.

About sixty new men have joined us to make up for our losses. They're straight from training camp and they know nothing. I feel a real old sweat by comparison. I don't feel as confident as I did two days ago. Now it's nearly here, I want it to be over.

24 JUNE 1916

REAR TRENCHES AT THE SOMME

This morning we moved up towards the line and no sooner had we reached the rear trenches than the British big guns opened up. I have never heard anything like it. The crash and crump of the guns, the wailing of the shells going over our heads, the explosions the other side of no man's land all scared the life out of me, so I daren't think what it does to the enemy. It goes on for hour after hour without ceasing. This must be what hell sounds like.

But for now, at night, it's stopped, so patrols can go out and see how much of the German wire is down. A nasty rumour has got back that most of it is still there. I hope that's not true. I'm using this blessed little time of quiet to write, while I can hear myself think and remember Jack dead at Loos and Mam and Dad back at home. If I hadn't joined up under age, I'd still be with them.

29 June 1916

The bombardment has continued all day, every day, for a week now. During the usual pause tonight, Colonel Elliott came into the huts to talk to us. We could see how pale and worried he looks. "Stick at it and you'll win a glorious victory," he said. "But I won't pretend that your task is not a huge one, greater than any army has ever before been called upon to do. God is with us and we shall win. But I would be failing in my duty if I did not say that tonight is a time to make your peace with the world and prepare to meet your maker if that is your fate."

Colonel Elliott is a good man and if he was making the plans instead of that stuck-up lot of staff officers back in some comfortable chateau, who never come with ten miles of the front if they can help it, we'd all be a lot happier.

30 June 1916
Front-line trench at the Somme

Today we had our last parade before going up to the front lines. Our rifles and bayonets were checked, ammunition and gas helmets handed out. On the way up to the first communication trench we saw pioneers digging a huge pit. We didn't have to be told what it was. A mass grave. After that, the march was terrible. The mud we squelched through became water coming up over our knees. Our kit weighed us down. Men kept falling and were lucky not to be trodden under and drowned.

At last we reached the trenches. They were in as big a mess as the flooded trenches we'd come through. But it's here we've got to stay and wait until the attack starts.

I pray that I'll get through this lot and not let myself down. I don't care any more whether we win. I just want to get out of here in one piece and back home again.

We've been put into four waves to go over the top tomorrow. I'm in the first wave. In a way, I'm glad. The attack starts at 7.30 in the morning. We hope. We were told the German artillery was destroyed. So who was firing at us this evening, hitting trenches and killing men before the attack has even started?

25 July 1916
1st Eastern General Hospital, Cambridge, England

Nearly a month has gone by since that dreadful first day on the Somme. Now I'm in England, in a military hospital in Cambridge. All this time I've been trying to piece together what happened to me and the rest of the battalion and now I'm going to write about it as best I can. The battle of the Somme is still raging and one thing is certain. We won't be in Berlin this year. Or any other year, I reckon.

That night before the attack started, we wrote letters home. If we were killed, the letters would be sent to our families for us. I thought of what it would be like in my parents' house if my letter was the last thing they had from me. Then we tried to get some sleep. We were worn out with marching and with the weight of our equipment. The noise of the bombardments, theirs and ours, was terrible. But I was so tired that I slept for a couple of hours standing up in mud with German shells falling round us – and some of our own as well, dropping short. Some men were killed and more wounded. When I woke, it was dreadful. I'd dreamt of home and I'd woken to this.

When the sun rose, we could see it would be a beautiful day. How strange it seemed that birds sang as if it was a morning like any other. I could see the German lines. They were well dug in, higher than us, so we would have to advance uphill. At 7.20, suddenly, the British guns stopped firing. I couldn't believe the silence. But ten minutes later, there were whistles and shouts from down the line, Captain Cunliffe blew his whistle and at last we had to climb out of the trenches.

Just for a second, I thought the staff officers might be right and all we had to do was walk across. Then the machine guns started. Our guns hadn't blasted the Germans away at all. They were waiting for us. This was it. I was sure I wouldn't get through the day.

We started the slow walk up the slope across no man's land. All I could hear was the terrifying rattle of their machine guns. The first person I saw fall was Captain Cunliffe, in front of me. Then I saw men dropping all round me. I just walked on. I passed Captain Cunliffe and saw that he was dead, though his eyes were still open as if he was willing me to go on. So I kept going. It was a miracle I wasn't hit, because there weren't many of us left standing now. This was a massacre.

I saw Sergeant Pickering shot. He dropped dead into the mud. We had nobody to lead us now. Of all people, I thought he would make it through. We came to a shell hole. I went round it to the right, the others went to the left. I felt a sudden searing pain in my leg and another in my shoulder.

The Big Push

The Somme, 1916

I'd been hit twice. I pulled myself up and looked. Nobody was still standing. Every one of them was dead. I didn't know what to do. And I didn't care any more.

Then a piece of shrapnel hit my rifle and made it spin away out of my hands into the shell hole. The German wire ahead looked like it hadn't been touched – when we'd been told it was flattened. Some of our men had reached it. But then I saw them killed as they tried to cut a way through and now their bodies were draped over that awful barbed wire. I couldn't go any further. I dropped into the shell hole, crawled after my rifle and hoped no German would drop a grenade on me.

There was someone else in the shell hole. He was moaning horribly. He had a wound in his head and his leg was a mess. I recognised him. He was Jack Ousely who used to deliver groceries on his bike. "Eh up, Billy," he said. Then I passed out. I don't know for how long. When I woke, Jack Ousely was staring at me as if he was waiting for me to come round. "I'm all right now, Jack," I said. Then I realised he was dead. Back in Todheaton, I'd never liked him much, but seeing him dead when he'd only joined up for a bit of fun like the rest of us made me cry at the waste of it all.

I don't remember anything after that. I knew

nothing more until I woke up in the Dressing Station behind the lines. A stretcher party found me and brought me back under fire, though they didn't think I had much hope. But then the Medical Officer came to look at me and my bandages.

"You're lucky to be here, soldier," he said. "It's Blighty for you." Thank God, I thought. Oh, thank you, thank you, God.

So I had somehow lived through a day which had been the very worst of the whole war. More than half the battalion were dead or wounded. I heard afterwards that it was just as bad along the whole front. There were seventy thousand killed and injured on that first day, nearly as many as go to watch the Cup Final, and it's still going on. We were on to a loser from the start.

I keep thinking of the German wire and my mates killed as they tried to cut through. There's a song we sing now and I can't get it out of my head:

"IF YOU WANT THE OLD BATTALION,
WE KNOW WHERE THEY ARE,
WE KNOW WHERE THEY ARE.

IF YOU WANT THE OLD BATTALION,
WE KNOW WHERE THEY ARE,

THEY'RE HANGING ON THE OLD
BARBED WIRE."

26 July 1916

In the casualty clearing station and then in the Advance Dressing Station, I saw many soldiers injured far worse than me. Some didn't last their first night behind the lines. I wasn't too bad. A doctor examined me and said, "A bullet has shattered the shin bone in your right leg but the leg isn't in danger. There's a bullet lodged in your right shoulder, but it won't be taken out until you're in hospital at Boulogne."

I was put on a hospital train and jolted along for twelve hours, in a proper carriage this time though it still seemed to have square wheels. By the time I reached the military hospital at Boulogne I must have passed out with the pain. When I came to, I was in a clean bed with white sheets. It seemed almost worth getting wounded just for that. They kept me without food and water all that first night, then, first thing in the morning, I was put under chloroform and when I woke up the bullet was out and my leg was splinted up and two nurses were smiling down at me. Their faces looked so calm and beautiful that my pain seemed to fade away. I had forgotten such sights could exist. The doctor who had operated on me was a major. "Well, soldier," he said. "There's no more war for you for a while. We'll send you back to hospital in England until you can walk, then you'll have a nice long leave. All those months ahead, walking out with your young lady."

That sounded wonderful. I should be happy. But I'm not. I haven't got a young lady and if I did, it wouldn't be fair on either of us. What future would there be in it for her if I have to go back to the trenches? I feel bad. I'm glad to be alive, but something tells me I should be with Captain Cunliffe, Sergeant Pickering, Jack Ousely, all the lads pinned to the barbed wire and thousands like them.

30 July 1916

This hospital is a pleasant place. We sleep in long huts, about thirty to a hut. The nurses are gentle with us and people from the town come round with "comforts for the troops", socks, cast-off clothing, fruit, biscuits and chocolates. I know they mean well, but I'm not the only one who feels he's being given charity. We don't like being pitied and we don't like being helpless. It was different when the French people gave us food as we marched. They were grateful because we were saving them. We saw it in their eyes. We don't see it in the eyes here.

4 August 1916

My nineteenth birthday. We had a big visit. Some government minister came to inspect, with a bishop and a lot of hangers-on in tow. What a birthday treat! Some of them looked to me as if they should be out in France. The hospital was

cleaned and polished until it gleamed and so were we. Flags of all the allied nations were hung from the ceiling. The man from the government praised us for our patriotism: "The country is proud of your noble heroism in a great and righteous cause and I know how impatient you are to be back with your comrades to face the foe."

The bishop led prayers for victory to be ours no matter what the sacrifice. I thought of the sacrifices made already by the Loyal Lancs and Yorks. By the time they had left we all wanted to be sick. I began to wonder what sort of country it was that I had come back to. Then I remembered that two years ago it was speeches like that which made me desperate to join up.

15 September 1916

I haven't written for a long time. I've been too busy getting my strength back in my leg and shoulder. My leg is still plastered up and I walk with a crutch. The doctor thinks my leg will always be a bit bent. "Still," he said. "It will show Fritz he can never keep a good man down." He laughed, but I didn't think it was funny. It wasn't his leg. Fritz is a good man as well and he goes through the same hell as us. I wonder if Fritz's people back in Germany talk such rot as the people here do?

29 September 1916

My plaster came off today. It was getting uncomfortable and smelly and made me howl when the hairs on my leg came off with it. Even so, I'm sorry to see it go because all the nurses had signed it, even the sister and matron. But the signature I prized most was Nurse Daisy Smith's. I like her and I think she likes me.

1 October 1916

Whenever she gets a moment to herself, which isn't often, Daisy comes over to have a chat. Yes, I really do like her. We've exchanged addresses for when I'm discharged from here. I remembered what the doctor said at Boulogne; all those months ahead walking out with my young lady. Perhaps Daisy could be my young lady. But should I say anything to her? Was it right, when they'll be sending me back and next time I might not be so lucky? All the more reason for looking after myself when I get back to France.

3 October 1916

They let me out of the hospital today to see how I could walk with a stick. It was Daisy's day off as well and when I asked her, she said she would come out with me. I was really happy about that. But when we were walking down the streets of

Cambridge I felt very strange. People were jostling round us living ordinary lives, as if there wasn't a war on. Some saw me and looked the other way, as if I made them feel guilty. I saw newspaper placards:

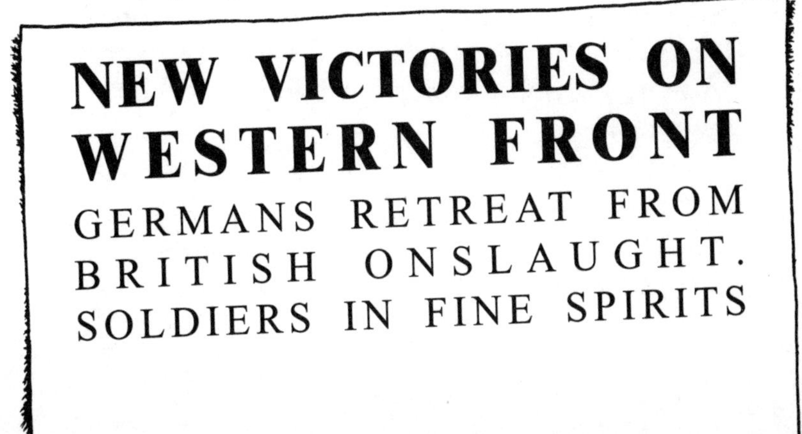

NEW VICTORIES ON WESTERN FRONT

GERMANS RETREAT FROM BRITISH ONSLAUGHT. SOLDIERS IN FINE SPIRITS

I wondered if they were talking about some other war that I hadn't been part of. In the evening we went to a music hall, where some big woman dressed as Britannia got the audience singing patriotic songs. I couldn't make myself join in. The man next to me saw and said, "Why aren't you singing? Are you a conchie or something?" Well, I'm not a conscientious objector, but I've seen enough needless waste of good men these last months to make me know why some refused to fight and were prepared to go to prison for it. I felt very angry.

Daisy could see how I felt. "Don't worry about people like him," she whispered. "They know nothing."

Now I'm back at the hospital I know two things. First, that Daisy really is my young lady and if I come through the war alive I want to be with her. But the second is this. All that matters to me now is to be back in France with my mates, because they are the only ones who count. My best friends have died or been wounded worse than me. We've been through the worst together but there's more to come and I won't let them down now.

18 October 1916
On the train leaving Cambridge

I'm on my way home. I've just said goodbye to Daisy. Though we didn't say much, I think we both know we want to get married when the war is over. As the train left Cambridge, seeing her standing alone on the platform waving goodbye to me was terrible. Will I ever see her again?

20 October 1916
Todheaton, Yorkshire

On leave at home. It's wonderful to see Mam and Dad. But sad as well. They look so old and worn out and somehow I can't say much any more. Now I know what Jack felt like on his last leave. Everybody tries to be nice and understanding but I just can't talk to them. Nobody who hasn't been there can understand what it's like in France and the trouble is I don't think anybody wants to. They'd rather believe what the papers tell them, that we keep on winning great victories.

22 October 1916

I went down to the pub with our Dad last night. When the regulars saw me, they gave a big cheer and everyone stood me a drink. At first everything was fine. I even heard that Fred Oughton was fully recovered from his wounds and back in France. But then Arthur Chadderton, who I knew from school, had a few too many and he really turned on me. "You lot can't do your jobs properly out in France, so they're pushing everyone in to the army whether we like it or not. Well, I don't like it. Burtons is making shells and guns now and we're earning good money with overtime, more than any of us have even seen. I can look after my family properly for the first time in my life, and because of you I have to give it all up."

I was angry with him. "You should have some guts and come out to help us," I said. "Making shells is women's work, at least it is in most places now." But I could see that some agreed with him. So I told Dad I wanted to go home. I get worried about what the army's going to be like in the future. We volunteered because we wanted to go. Now men like Arthur will have to go whether they want to or not.

23 October 1916

I went out with Dad last night, so I ought to do the same with Mam. I took her to the pictures. We saw one funny film, with a comedian I'd heard about called Charlie Chaplin. It wasn't bad, though I didn't like the lovey-dovey sort of film on with it. But then they showed a newsreel and that made me angry. All these happy troops marching along singing. It's a good job there's no sound. People might be surprised at the words they were putting to the songs. Then they

showed this incredible new weapon which was going to win us the war because it scared the Germans to death. It's called the tank. I'd never heard of it and it didn't look much cop to me anyway, great clumsy thing.
I'll believe it when
I see it.

27 October 1916

My leave is over. I'm on my way back to France. It was hard leaving home, though I didn't feel comfortable there these last few days.

I'm writing in a railway carriage lit by flickering gas lamps. I've got a "wound stripe" sewn on my sleeve, so now everyone will know I've seen some action. There are soldiers all round me going back to France but we don't talk much. I think we're all too busy with our own thoughts. I try to think of Daisy and the life we'll have together when the war's over, but it's hard. I can't believe it will ever come to an end and when I look round the carriage and see all those pale, set faces, I don't think anyone else here does either. The only bright spot is that I might team up with Fred again.

30 October 1916
Amiens, Northern France

I've rejoined the Twenty-fifth Battalion, the old Todheaton Pals, in billets near Amiens. We're being kept in reserve. We're under strength and I'm one of the very last to be left of the original Pals who joined up in the first month of the war. New men are coming in all the time. Some are conscripts who never wanted to be here. Some are from other battalions. Many don't come from anywhere near Todheaton. Except for Colonel Elliott (and the staff officers back in the chateaux, who never even cut their fingers) none of our old officers are still alive. The new ones come from London, Scotland, Cornwall, anywhere, it seems bar Yorkshire and Lancashire.

5 November 1916

Wonderful. I've met up with Fred Oughton. They patched him up and sent him back and here he is. He seems his cheery old self again. "Billy," he cried. "I heard you'd copped it at the Somme." We were so pleased to see each other alive and fit - well, fit enough for this mob.

Fred showed me the two wound stripes on his sleeve. "That night of the trench raid I copped two bullets, one right in my guts and the other in my leg," he said. "The doc said half an inch either way and the one in my belly would have done for me. I nearly had to have my leg off as well, but they saved it. It took them a long time to get me right, but if I can get through that lot I can get through anything. Fritz can't hurt me now. You stick by me, young Billy, and you'll not go far wrong."

He made me feel good, even though I knew he was bluffing. But we wish Tommy Braithwaite was with us to make up our threesome.

30 December 1916

It's freezing here. Thank God we aren't out in the trenches. Over Christmas we were billeted in huts which aren't too bad and we had a pretty fair time. Let someone else do the fighting for a change, we all thought. Except for football and boxing to keep our spirits up, it's training, training all the time, so when they finally want us for the fighting, you can be sure it's going to be something big.

A new year tomorrow. Pray God it will be the last year of this horrible war. Let's hope for better things ahead.

20 JANUARY, 1917

Snow, ice, ice, snow. I've never known weather so cold. It's the worst winter I've ever been through.

I've often heard rumours which I don't like to think about too much, of soldiers being shot for cowardice. It's never happened in the Todheaton Pals, as far as I know. But Reg Woolley, who came to us from a London regiment which was badly shot up on the Somme, had a terrible tale to tell. There was this young lad whose nerve cracked when the British guns stopped, ten minutes before the battalion was about to go over the top. He started screaming and threw his rifle away. Reg said he thought the officer in charge was going to shoot him there and then, but instead he shoved him into a dugout and put him under armed guard while he sent a message back to brigade to take him back behind the lines, under arrest. When the attack was over and Reg had got back safe, the lad was court martialled and sentenced to be shot for cowardice.

They did it next morning at dawn. "I know that because I was there," said Reg. "I was detailed to be on the firing party. He was only a young lad who was frightened. So were we all, but he couldn't keep it to himself. I feel sick whenever I think about it."

I'd rather stand up to the worst that Fritz can do than face that.

27 March, 1917

I've not written these last months. We've all been too tense. We've stayed in reserve in our billets, waiting for another big push. We must have done something right last year on the Somme because the Germans have retreated. Many of the places we lost so many men fighting for, we've taken now just by walking into them and finding nobody there. Still, from what we know about our enemy, he'll have dug himself in deep in the best place. It means we'll have another terrible time trying to winkle him out.

But now we're to leave the wooden huts we've got used to. We're moving up to Arras because soon the next big battle is going to start. Tonight I wrote to Mam and Dad and then I wrote to Daisy. After last year on the Somme I know what to expect, so I didn't tell them too much except sending them all my love. Anyway, if I had, the censor would have crossed it out.

29 March 1917

A village ten miles west of Arras, Northern France

There's still snow on the ground after that awful winter, though it's beginning to thaw. A thaw means more mud, and in the trenches that's not good to look forward to. We marched all yesterday and all today, through coalfields and ruined villages. Already we can see the big guns moving up for the bombardment of the German trenches which always comes before us poor infantrymen attack. We can hear the booming of the guns already there, ours and, you can be sure, the Germans' as well.

10 April 1917
Arras

We're in trenches just east of Arras. Behind us is the town, with all its people sheltering in cellars from the German shells. Poor beggars.

Somewhere ahead of us is where the Germans have dug themselves in. We call it the Hindenburg Line and you may be sure it will be hard to take. We reckon they'll use poison gas there. The Todheaton Pals have faced most things but not gas yet, and from what I hear I don't want to. But there's also some great news! It really perks us up a bit. For once the bombardment must have worked. The Canadians yesterday stormed Vimy Ridge and took it, with very few of their men being killed. If they can do it, so can we.

We've been told that this time we're going in protected by the big guns in a way we weren't before. We've got more aeroplanes now, to bomb the Germans and observe their movements. To me, though, they don't seem much use. But there's also the tank, this thing I saw on the newsreel back home. Men in tanks will advance with us.

15 April 1917
Field Hospital, Arras

Would you believe it? Back in the field hospital. I never even got out of the trench. The moment I stood on the parapet a bullet got me in the left shoulder this time and knocked me backwards. Lucky? You bet. It could have got me in the head.

I was taken back behind the lines and the bullet was taken out there. Sadly, though, the wound isn't too bad, so no Blighty this time and no chance to see Daisy. They'll just send me to a convalescent hospital behind the lines and get me back as soon as they can. There won't be anything worth putting in my diary so I'll spend my time writing home and to Daisy. Anyway, I didn't miss much. The attack got beaten back and the tanks stuck in the mud.

5 June 1917
South of Ypres, Belgium

I'm back in the trenches. We've got a new sergeant and a new corporal who have been in this lot from the first and somehow got through so we all trust them. It doesn't seem right that they have to take orders from our new company commander, an officer who's as young as I am and just come out from Blighty, from his public school. Lieutenant Anstruther-Boyd, his name is, and he doesn't seem to know anything.

Fred is with me again, still surviving. Reg Woolley, our mate from London, copped it in the last attack. We're in trenches south of Ypres. I don't know what the Belgians call it but we call it "Wipers". There have been two battles here already, so there's not much of it left. We're in front of another German position. It's looking down on us from a place called Messines Ridge. We're going to attack it soon, but there are rumours that before we go over the top something big is going to happen. We do know that there's been a lot of tunnelling from our trenches under no man's land to the German lines. When I think of those poor blokes digging tunnels towards the German lines and the Germans digging their way towards ours, I shudder. I'd rather be up here and stop a bullet than be down there and get buried alive in tons of earth. But they *are* up to something down there. We'll have to wait and see what it is.

6 June 1917

I can't believe what I've just seen. It was 3.10 in the afternoon. We were waiting in the trench watching the Messines Ridge, when suddenly it was as if everything in front of us exploded. Earth, rocks, flames and smoke rose into the air three hundred feet and more. A split second later came a deafening roar and the ground shook beneath us. For a moment it was like the end of the world.

Then we realised that was what the tunnelling was for. Huge mines were laid under the German trenches and when they went off the whole lot blew up. When the noise had died down everybody was quiet. We knew that mines were often laid, by the Germans as well as us, and sometimes trenches had been blown up with the men in them.

But this was tremendous. I know they were our enemies, but the thought of those hundreds of men suddenly being blown to bits made us all think.

The noise kept on, though this time it was our guns with their crashing bombardment. We waited.

Then Lieutenant Anstruther-Boyd gave the order, "Fix bayonets."

We scrambled out of the trench, him leading with his revolver ready, and walked towards the huge craters left by the explosions. The floors of the craters were full of fire and we skirted them warily. Black smoke drifted round us and there was some shooting yet we kept going. Nobody seemed to be falling. There were no Germans left to attack us except a few who seemed only too pleased to be taken prisoner. We moved past those awful fiery pits and took our new positions in trenches beyond. The easiest day I'd ever had in an attack. But we aren't fooled. The Germans won't let us get away with that.

That was snooty Lieutenant Anstruther-Boyd's first time in no man's land. I hope he doesn't think it's always going to be like that.

30 July 1917

Behind the lines, Passchendaele

There's so much happening lately that I haven't had a chance to write. Now we're getting ready to move up into the line again, for the big attack. It's been raining and the trenches will be knee-deep in water again. We could drown in the shell craters, but the officers say we're on top now in this war and nothing can stop us. This time, they may just be right. The barrage from our guns is so loud you can't hear yourself speak. They say this battle is going to be as big as the Somme but this time it's going to work. I hope so. I might get out alive to see my Daisy.

31 July 1917
Front-line trench, Passchendaele

A day spent waiting in the firing trench. It's us who have to attack first. Yesterday I felt quite good. Today I don't.

The officers can say what they like, but I have a bad feeling inside me and it's not to do with lice, trench foot or eating cold Maconochies. This is an awful place. The rain has stopped now, but it has been so heavy for days on end that the ground is churned into swamps by shells which dropped short. As always, we've got to advance uphill because when the Germans retreat they choose their new positions well. We can see their plan. They want us to destroy ourselves trying to take their trenches while they mow us down with their machine guns. It's happened before and it's going to happen again.

I've been looking back through this diary. It's not three years since I started it, but I can't believe I was the same person then. In four days' time this war will have been going on for three years and I will be twenty. I should be in Todheaton playing football and cricket with my mates and working at Burtons. That's what happened to lads like me before and it's what will happen to them in the future. Why did it have to be Fred and Tommy and me and the thousands like me who were different? What sort of fate said it had to be us?

We'll be going over the top tomorrow. I've written letters to Mam and Dad and to Daisy. I can't do any more except pray that I'll come out of it near enough in one piece. Actually, Anstruther-Boyd has shown that he's all right. I trust him. But I'm sticking close to Fred. We're best mates, we've been through a lot together and he'll look out for me, just as I'll look out for him. Whatever the outcome, I don't suppose anybody will forget what happens tomorrow at Passchendaele.

BRITISH ARMY FIELD HOSPITAL
ARRAS

7th August, 1917

Dear Mr and Mrs Warren

It is my sad duty to inform you that your son, Private W J Warren, was killed in the assault by the Todheaton Battalion on the German positions at Passchendaele. I can tell you that he advanced unflinchingly into intense enemy fire, although all round him he could see that the battalion was taking heavy losses. He was a fine soldier and an example to his comrades. As an officer new to the battalion, he was one of the men experienced in battle to whom I looked for inspiration.

Please accept my condolences and sorrow at the death of such a steadfast comrade and very fine man.

Yours sincerely,

J Anstruther-Boyd (Lieutenant)

BRITISH ARMY FIELD HOSPITAL
ARRAS

10th August, 1917

Dear Mr and Mrs Warren,

I have to write to you to let you know about Billy. On the day of the attack we went over the top first thing in the morning. Anstruther-Boyd blew his whistle and led us out. The moment we were through our wire the Germans opened up but we kept going. Billy and I stuck together like we always did. I could see our lads going down like ninepins, but Anstruther-Boyd was still ahead and we were up there with him. Then I saw that Billy was hit.

I stopped and so did Anstruther-Boyd. But we could see Billy had bought it, so we kept on going. Then Anstruther-Boyd copped it in the knee and I got another nasty one which meant I've had my left arm taken off. So that's put me out of the war for good. We waited with shells falling all round us until night came. Then the stretcher bearers came out and got us back.

When I'm home I'll be round to see you. Billy was my best mate and when he joined up with Tommy and me all that time ago, we never thought it would come to this. There's nobody left of the old Todheaton Battalion. Billy and me were the last.

I've written a note to Daisy as well, because someone's got to let her know.

Yours truly,

Fred

1ST EASTERN GENERAL HOSPITAL
CAMBRIDGE

20th August, 1917

Dear Mr and Mrs Warren,

I'm so sorry to hear about Billy being killed at Passchendaele. I really liked Billy. I thought he was the nicest of all the wounded soldiers who were ever sent here. I hoped I would soon come to Todheaton and meet you both. Billy and I had already said that when this war was over we would get married, but now that is not to be.

I know that many thousands of good young men have been killed and I feel sorry for all of them. But Billy was special to me, and I shall never, *never* forget him for as long as I live.

I know what you are feeling, especially as you have now lost both your sons. I have lost a brother and now the man I wanted to marry, so we have all been badly treated by this horrible war.

Yours sincerely,

Daisy (Smith)

WHAT LED UP TO THE FIRST WORLD WAR?

The twentieth century was full of terrible wars: Vietnam, Korea, the Falklands, the Gulf War and lots more. But the worst of all were the two world wars, from 1914 to 1918 and 1939 to 1945. The First World War was called "the war to end wars." But it didn't turn out like that.

Nearly fifty years before, in 1870, there had been a war between France and Germany or Prussia as it was then before all the German states were united into one country. The Prussians won. The French had to agree to let them have Alsace Lorraine, an area to the south of France with valuable iron and steel industries. The French itched for revenge. They wanted Alsace Lorraine back. So everybody knew that sooner or later there would be another war between the two.

HOW DID BRITAIN GET INVOLVED?

It's hard for us to understand now, but people all over Europe really seemed to want a war. For many years there had been lots of very popular novels about wars in the future between Britain and Germany.

Why were these fictional wars always

between Britain and Germany? When Britain had fought in a European war before, it had usually been against France. Now, though, Britain and France were allies and had signed a treaty of friendship called the *Entente Cordiale*.

In the nineteenth century Britain had been the world's strongest nation. It ruled over a great Empire, consisting of the countries which are now called the British Commonwealth. It also had its industry. Britain was then called the "workshop of the world", and was the first country to make the steamships and railway engines.

But Germany was catching up fast. Also, Germany was not a collection of small countries any more. Count Bismarck, the Prussian Chancellor, had united them into the largest, most powerful nation in Europe. Some people said the rivalry between Britain and Germany meant that in the end, one would have to wipe the other out.

So, different countries were busy making alliances, pledging to come to each others' aid if they were attacked. Britain joined up with France, Russia and Italy and also smaller countries such as Belgium and Serbia. They became the "Allied Powers". Germany made agreements with Austria and its empire in eastern Europe, Bulgaria and Turkey. They became the "Central Powers".

Meanwhile, factories were making more fearful and deadly weapons. One of these weapons was the battleship called the Dreadnought, the biggest and best armed that the world had ever seen.

When the British government said it could not afford to build an eighth Dreadnought in peace time, people marched through the streets chanting *"We want eight and we won't wait."* They wanted to be equipped for war. So, by 1914, the European powers had the means to wage the most horrible, bloodiest and stupid war yet.

It was bound to come, yet when it did, it still took ordinary people by surprise. Strangely, though, they were pleased. Britain had a huge navy and an efficient army. Lots of young men, working in factories, banks, shops and down coal mines, longed to join the army and have some adventure. An exciting war, then home for Christmas? They thought that would be wonderful!

HOW DID IT ALL START?

The Emperor Franz Joseph of Austria ruled over many other countries in Europe as well. The Austrian Empire was made up of Hungary, Romania, Slovakia, what we now call the Czech Republic, parts of Italy and Poland and some countries in the Balkans too. However the countries nearby didn't want to be forced to become part of that empire under Emperor Joseph's rule. One of these countries was Serbia. So, the thing that started off the First World War happened when a Serbian terrorist called Gavrilo Princip assassinated the heir to the throne of the Austrian Empire, Archduke Ferdinand. Austria immediately declared war on Serbia.

Now, all the alliances came into play. Russia came in on the side of the Serbs. France came in on the side of Russia. Germany attacked France at once. To get there her army marched through Belgium. Britain had an agreement that if ever Belgium was invaded, she would declare war on that invader. So Britain declared war on Germany.

So there it was. As soon as the Archduke Ferdinand was murdered, the countries in Europe were ready for war with each other.

WHAT HAPPENED?

Although there were new and modern weapons, army generals still thought war would be like it was in the days of Napoleon and Wellington. Armies would move quickly from place to place, there would be big battles, which resulted in a clear victory for one side or the other.

But everything turned out differently in the First World War because of the Germans' new idea – the Schlieffen Plan. Their plan was to march through Belgium in a great arc and capture Paris from the north. At first, the Germans' plan worked well because the French didn't realise what the German strategy was. They tried to attack the German army, but not very successfully. As the French soldiers wore old-fashioned red and blue uniforms instead of khaki like everybody else, the Germans could see them coming from miles off. At last, however, the French understood what the German plan was.

The British Army joined the French and they managed to stop the Germans, by then close to Paris. Then both sides made the "race to the sea" to try and gain control of the ports along the English Channel.

Within three months, both sides had dug trenches all the way from the Belgian coast, through northern France and almost to Switzerland and they stayed there for four years, with no idea how they could get any further. For four more years they expended men and material in these trenches, gaining a few hundred yards of ground and then losing it again.

THE BRITISH ARMY

Britain is an island. Everybody thought Britain would never be invaded by an enemy power. She did not have a big army like other countries in Europe, preferring instead to have a huge navy. Instead, there was a small, professional army of regular soldiers called the British Expeditionary Force (BEF), ready to go out and fight short wars. There was also the Territorial Army, in which men learnt to be soldiers in their spare time after work but had to be ready to fight with the regular army in emergencies. It was soon clear that this wasn't enough. Lord Kitchener, the Army Chief of Staff, proposed a great volunteer New Army. The response was huge. Men flooded in. Cities and towns recruited their own battalions, the "Pals".

Even this wasn't enough. So great was the loss of life in the first two years of war that in 1916 conscription had to begin. Conscription meant that every able-bodied man had to join the army. There was no choice. Those whose consciences would not let them fight, the "conscientious objectors", were either put in prison or made to be stretcher bearers. People called them "conchies". They had to put up with a lot of abuse.

THE TRENCHES

Because the Germans had given the war some thought before they fought it, they were much better prepared than their enemies. Once their first attack had failed, they chose high ground to defend so the British and French had to climb uphill to get at them. They dug deep, safe trenches. They had more machine guns and set them up to kill as many soldiers advancing up the slopes as they could. This way, they thought they would destroy the British and French armies and conquer France.

The British and French thought that they would batter the German trenches until they themselves could break through to advance on to Berlin, the capital of Germany. For years, generals and their staff officers, who never went near the trenches, thought that if enough men walked in straight lines towards the trenches, in the end they would get through. They never did. The Germans picked them off with machine guns.

The British and French trenches were always dug quickly, because the Germans had got theirs done first. British and French trenches were shallower. British trenches, dug in low-lying land, flooded quickly. The soldiers lined the trenches with sandbags. In front of the trenches, barbed wire was fixed to posts in a network to a depth of twenty or thirty metres so that invading soldiers could not break through. Both sides were very careful about their wire because it was so important to the defence of their trenches. The land between the trenches was called "no man's land".

THE SOLDIERS

When they were in the front line, soldiers lived, ate and slept in the trenches. The conditions were terrible. They were assailed by rats and lice, they sank and sometimes drowned in mud. They lived among the partly-buried bodies of soldiers killed in previous battles.

They were called out to go in patrols in no man's land. They also had to do sentry duty in trenches called "saps" which were dug far out into no man's land. All this while waiting to "go over the top" in the next great attack, which until the very last one, ended in failure.

The worst disaster was the Battle of the Somme, the first day of which saw Billy Warren injured. It was the most carefully planned military operation ever known and a complete failure. Nearly 70,000 British soldiers were killed or wounded on the first day of the battle. It is still the worst calamity in the history of the British Army.

The soldiers in the front line, like Billy, were called *infantry*. Behind them was the *artillery*. The artillery fired the really big guns. Before an attack by the infantry, the artillery bombarded the enemy lines.

The idea was that everybody in the opposite trenches would be killed, their barbed wire broken up by the exploding shells and the infantry could just walk in and capture their trenches. The strategy never worked. The gunfire did not reach the Germans in their deep, well-dug trenches and their barbed wire stayed in place.

WHAT ABOUT THE NAVY?

The Royal Navy waited a long time to do battle with the German Grand Fleet. Both fleets seemed unwilling to face each other. To lose such a great sea battle might lose the whole war. When it finally happened, at Jutland in 1916, the huge battleships fired at and sank each other so the final result was no more than a draw. These big ships never faced each other again for fear that they would *all* be sunk.

WHAT ABOUT THE WAR IN THE AIR?

For most of the war, British airmen belonged to the Royal Flying Corps, which was part of the Army. The Royal Air Force was formed shortly before the end of the war. Their stringy little biplanes were used for observation and for fighting the Germans' equally small planes.

There were many battles in the sky and the first fighter "aces" appeared, shooting down many enemy planes in "dogfights". Albert Ball was a British fighter ace and the Red Baron, Baron von Richthofen, in his bright red Fokker Triplane, was a fighter ace for the Germans.

WHAT ABOUT THE WAR IN OTHER PLACES?

Germany was also fighting Russia in the east. The Russian army was not well equipped. Therefore this war was easier for the Germans. In 1917, the Bolshevik Revolution brought Lenin and the Communists to power in Russia. Russia then left the war. Germany was now free to concentrate on the western front.

There was also war between Britain and Turkey in the Dardanelles, by the Black Sea. Australian and New Zealand troops were involved. This campaign was a failure, with thousands of needless deaths. Fairly soon it was called off and Allied troops recalled to France.

Meanwhile, the Austrians attacked Italy via the Alps, while the British sent troops round the world to defend parts of her empire threatened by the Germans.
Truly, the world was in chaos.

WHAT FINISHED THE WAR?

Two things. First, in 1915, a German U-boat torpedoed the *Lusitania,* a passenger liner, crowded with Americans. Many United States citizens drowned. This was the last straw for the United States though it was two years before American troops crossed the Atlantic to France to join the allies.

The arrival of new, fresh, well-armed soldiers was well-timed, because France had lost a huge number of men. However, Germany no longer had to worry about fighting the Russians and could use her whole army against the French and British.

In March 1918 it seemed as though the Germans had won. They broke through the British and French defences. It looked as though the Allies were finished. But the Germans too were exhausted and they could not sustain their advance any further.

Then came what many say was the finest campaign the British Army ever fought. At this point hardly any of the original British Expeditionary Force were left. The army consisted almost entirely of volunteers and conscripts. They advanced through bitter fighting out of France and into Germany. Soon the Germans realised they could not defend themselves any more. On November 11th, 1918 they gave up and the Armistice (peace treaty) was signed.

BACK AT HOME

Nothing could ever be the same, surely? With the men away, women had done their work for the first time, making shells, guns and tanks which proved to be very powerful weapons. They had gone to the front as nurses and sometimes died there. Now they wanted freedom, starting with the vote.

Meanwhile, in the army and navy, miners had fought alongside lords and farm labourers had died next to bankers. Surely this would make a difference. Would there not be a great change in Britain now?

No, there wasn't. No sooner had peace come than influenza crossed Europe. In a world without antibiotics, this killed nearly as many people as the war had. British soldiers came home to find there were no new homes, no work – in fact nothing had changed. It took until the end of the Second World War in 1945 for things to change.

WHAT HAPPENED AFTERWARDS?

There was a great conference held at Versailles. Prime Minister Lloyd George of Britain, President Clemenceau of France and Woodrow Wilson, President of the United States, had one aim – to humiliate Germany and cripple the German economy. They imposed huge debts to make up for the damage that had been done. Well, they crippled and humiliated Germany – but forgot one thing. If you do that to people, they bite back. By the 1930s, the poverty stricken German people were ready to vote for any leader who promised them better times and a return to their former greatness. So now they were ready to vote in – *Adolf Hitler.*

1914 - 1918.

The war to end wars?

Fat chance.

BILLY WARREN

There were hundreds of thousands of boys like Billy who cheerfully went to war and never came back. Everything that happens in his diary is based on a true event.

Other titles in this series

The diary of a Young Roman Soldier

Marcus Gallo travels to Britain with his legion to help pacify the wild Celtic tribes.

The diary of a Young Tudor Lady-in-Waiting

Young Rebecca Swann joins her aunt as a lady-in-waiting at the court of Queen Elizabeth the First.

The diary of a Victorian Apprentice

Samuel Cobbett becomes an apprentice at a factory making steam locomotives.

The diary of a Young Nurse in World War II

Jean Harris is hired to train as a nurse in a London hospital just as World War II breaks out.

The diary of a Young Elizabethan Actor

William Savage is a boy actor during the last years of the reign of Queen Elizabeth the First.

The diary of a Young West Indian Immigrant

It is 1957 and Gloria Charles travels from Dominica in the West Indies to start a new life in Britain.

The diary of a 1960s Teenager

It is 1965 and teenager Jane Leachman is offered a job working in swinging London's fashion industry.